Ten Pens

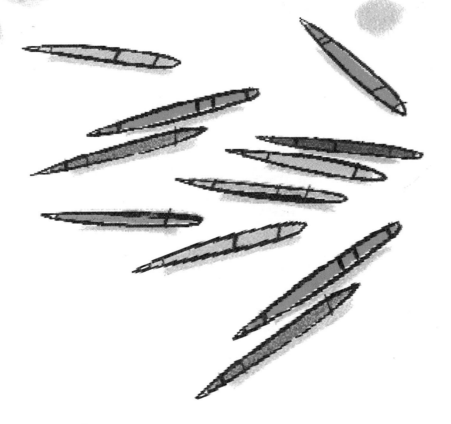

Ten Pens

Written by Su Yi Kim
Illustrated by Steve Salerno

SCHOLASTIC INC.

New York   Toronto   London   Auckland   Sydney
Mexico City   New Delhi   Hong Kong   Buenos Aires

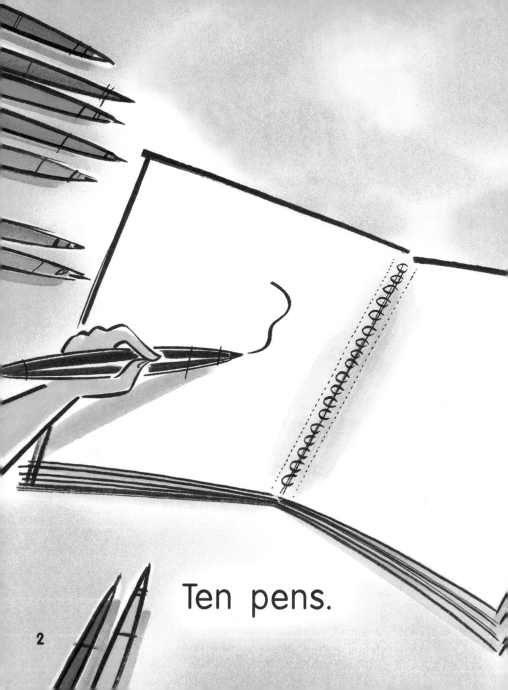

Ten pens.

Ten fat hens.

Ten tops.

Ten fans.

Ten cats in the sun.

Ten hats on ten men.

Can you see ten?

My ten pens.

ISBN-13: 978-0-545-06961-8
ISBN-10: 0-545-06961-0

Text copyright © 2003 by Scholastic Inc. Illustrations copyright © 2003 by Steve Salerno. All rights reserved. Published by Scholastic Inc. SCHOLASTIC, SCHOLASTIC READINGLINE, and associated logos are trademarks and/or registered trademarks of Scholastic Inc.

12 11 10 9 8 7 6 5 4 3 2 1   8 9 10 11 12 13/0

Printed in the U.S.A.   23

This edition first printing, March 2008